THE
READING WOMAN
2008 ENGAGEMENT CALENDAR

Pomegranate

7 17195 21841 6

Catalog No. Z221

Published by Pomegranate Communications, Inc.
Box 808022, Petaluma CA 94975

Available in the UK and mainland Europe from Pomegranate Europe Ltd.
Unit 1, Heathcote Business Centre, Hurlbutt Road, Warwick, Warwickshire CV34 6TD, UK

© 2007 Pomegranate Communications, Inc.
Photographs courtesy The Bridgeman Art Library, New York

Pomegranate also publishes the 2008 wall calendars *The Reading Woman*, *Carl Larsson*, and *Gardens of the Impressionists*, as well as many other calendars in several formats. Our products and publications include books; posters; postcards, books of postcards, and boxed postcard sets; notecards, notecard folios, and boxed notecard sets; magnets; mousepads; Knowledge Cards®; birthday books; journals; address books; jigsaw puzzles; designer gift wrap; stationery sets; and bookmarks. For more information or to place an order, please contact Pomegranate Communications, Inc.: 800 227 1428; www.pomegranate.com.

Cover image:
August Macke (German, 1887–1914)
Elisabeth Reading, n.d.
Pfalzgalerie, Kaiserslautern, Germany
Photograph courtesy The Bridgeman Art Library, New York

Designed by Mariah Lander
Conceived by Maxine Rose Schur

Dates in color indicate US federal holidays.

Dates listed for all astronomical events in this calendar are based on Universal Time (UT), the worldwide system of civil timekeeping. Universal Time is essentially equivalent to Greenwich Mean Time.

Moon phases and American, Canadian, and UK holidays are noted.

 NEW MOON   FIRST QUARTER   FULL MOON   LAST QUARTER

ARTISTS REPRESENTED IN THIS CALENDAR

Harriet Backer

Marie Bashkirtseff

Edward Burne-Jones

Jacques Cancaret

Lovis Corinth

Jean-Baptiste-Camille Corot

Georges Croegaert

Frank Dicey

Jean-Georges Ferry

Nikolay Nikolayevich Ge

Gwendolyn Grant

Jean-Baptiste-Armand Guillaumin

William Hatherell

Hans Olaf Heyerdahl

Carl Vilhelm Holsøe

Peter Vilhelm Ilsted

Peter Kraemer

Peder Severin Krøyer

Edmund Blair Leighton

George Dunlop Leslie

August Macke

Alexander Mann

Piero di Cosimo

Edward John Poynter

Pierre-Auguste Renoir

Hubert Salentin

Karl Maria Schuster

Alfred-Émile-Léopold Stevens

Félix Vallotton

Jan Vermeer

2008

JANUARY

s	m	t	w	t	f	s
		1	2	3	4	5
6	7	8	9	10	11	12
13	14	15	16	17	18	19
20	21	22	23	24	25	26
27	28	29	30	31		

FEBRUARY

s	m	t	w	t	f	s
					1	2
3	4	5	6	7	8	9
10	11	12	13	14	15	16
17	18	19	20	21	22	23
24	25	26	27	28	29	

MARCH

s	m	t	w	t	f	s
						1
2	3	4	5	6	7	8
9	10	11	12	13	14	15
16	17	18	19	20	21	22
$^{23}/_{30}$	$^{24}/_{31}$	25	26	27	28	29

APRIL

s	m	t	w	t	f	s
		1	2	3	4	5
6	7	8	9	10	11	12
13	14	15	16	17	18	19
20	21	22	23	24	25	26
27	28	29	30			

MAY

s	m	t	w	t	f	s
				1	2	3
4	5	6	7	8	9	10
11	12	13	14	15	16	17
18	19	20	21	22	23	24
25	26	27	28	29	30	31

JUNE

s	m	t	w	t	f	s
1	2	3	4	5	6	7
8	9	10	11	12	13	14
15	16	17	18	19	20	21
22	23	24	25	26	27	28
29	30					

2008

JULY

s	m	t	w	t	f	s
		1	2	3	4	5
6	7	8	9	10	11	12
13	14	15	16	17	18	19
20	21	22	23	24	25	26
27	28	29	30	31		

AUGUST

s	m	t	w	t	f	s
					1	2
3	4	5	6	7	8	9
10	11	12	13	14	15	16
17	18	19	20	21	22	23
$^{24}/_{31}$	25	26	27	28	29	30

SEPTEMBER

s	m	t	w	t	f	s
	1	2	3	4	5	6
7	8	9	10	11	12	13
14	15	16	17	18	19	20
21	22	23	24	25	26	27
28	29	30				

OCTOBER

s	m	t	w	t	f	s
			1	2	3	4
5	6	7	8	9	10	11
12	13	14	15	16	17	18
19	20	21	22	23	24	25
26	27	28	29	30	31	

NOVEMBER

s	m	t	w	t	f	s
						1
2	3	4	5	6	7	8
9	10	11	12	13	14	15
16	17	18	19	20	21	22
$^{23}/_{30}$	24	25	26	27	28	29

DECEMBER

s	m	t	w	t	f	s
	1	2	3	4	5	6
7	8	9	10	11	12	13
14	15	16	17	18	19	20
21	22	23	24	25	26	27
28	29	30	31			

I think we ought to read only the kind of book that wound and stab us. . . . We need the books that affect us like a disaster, that grieve us deeply, like the death of someone we loved more than ourselves, like being banished into forests far from everyone, like a suicide. A book must be the axe for the frozen sea inside us.
—Franz Kafka (1883–1924), letter to Oskar Pollak, 27 January 1904

Peter Vilhelm Ilsted (Danish, 1861–1933)
Woman Reading by Candlelight, 1908
Oil on canvas, 47 x 38.5 cm (18½ x 15³⁄₁₆ in.)
Connaught Brown, London
Photograph courtesy The Bridgeman Art Library, New York

JANUARY

SUNDAY	MONDAY	TUESDAY	WEDNESDAY	THURSDAY	FRIDAY	SATURDAY
		1	2	3	4	5
6	7	8 ●	9	10	11	12
13	14	15 ☽	16	17	18	19
20	21	22 ○	23	24	25	26
27	28	29	30 ☾	31		

JAN 1   NEW YEAR'S DAY
JAN 2   BANK HOLIDAY (SCOTLAND)

JAN 15   MARTIN LUTHER KING
           JR.'S BIRTHDAY
JAN 21   MARTIN LUTHER KING JR. DAY

DEC/JAN

monday
365   31 ☾

tuesday   NEW YEAR'S DAY
1   1

wednesday   BANK HOLIDAY (SCOTLAND)
2   2

thursday
3   3

friday
4   4

saturday
5   5

sunday
6   6

JANUARY

monday
7 7

tuesday
● **8** 8

wednesday
9 9

thursday
10 10

friday
11 11

saturday
12 12

s	m	t	w	t	f	s
		1	2	3	4	5
6	7	8	9	10	11	12
13	14	15	16	17	18	19
20	21	22	23	24	25	26
27	28	29	30	31		

sunday
13 13

My diary is a mirror telling the story of a dreamer who, a long long time ago, went through life the way one reads a book.
—Anaïs Nin, attributed

Jacques Cancaret (French, fl. 1904–1932)
Repose, n.d.
Oil on canvas
Private collection
Photograph courtesy The Bridgeman Art Library, New York

JANUARY

monday
14 14

tuesday
MARTIN LUTHER KING JR.'S BIRTHDAY
☽ 15 15

wednesday
16 16

thursday
17 17

friday
18 18

saturday
19 19

s	m	t	w	t	f	s
		1	2	3	4	5
6	7	8	9	10	11	12
13	14	15	16	17	18	19
20	21	22	23	24	25	26
27	28	29	30	31		

sunday
20 20

What a sense of superiority it gives one to escape reading some book which every one else is reading.

—Alice James, attributed

William Hatherell (English, 1855–1928)
A Quiet Spot, 1891
Watercolor, 30.5 x 49.5 cm (12 x 19½ in.)
Private collection

JANUARY

monday
21 ₂₁

MARTIN LUTHER KING JR. DAY

tuesday
○ ## 22 ₂₂

wednesday
23 ₂₃

thursday
24 ₂₄

friday
25 ₂₅

saturday
26 ₂₆

s	m	t	w	t	f	s
		1	2	3	4	5
6	7	8	9	10	11	12
13	14	15	16	17	18	19
20	21	22	23	24	25	26
27	28	29	30	31		

sunday
27 ₂₇

JAN/FEB

monday
28 28

tuesday
29 29

wednesday
30 30 ☾

thursday
31 31

friday
32 1

saturday
33 2

sunday
34 3

FEBRUARY

SUNDAY	MONDAY	TUESDAY	WEDNESDAY	THURSDAY	FRIDAY	SATURDAY
					1	2
3	4	5	6	7 ●	8	9
10	11	12	13	14 ☽	15	16
17	18	19	20	21 ○	22	23
24	25	26	27	28	29 ☾	

FEB 6   ASH WEDNESDAY
FEB 12   LINCOLN'S BIRTHDAY
FEB 14   VALENTINE'S DAY

FEB 18   PRESIDENTS' DAY
FEB 22   WASHINGTON'S BIRTHDAY

Persons still living remember a woman in Strathspey, who, though never taught to read, could recite the whole book of Psalms in the Gaelic translation, merely by having it read to her by others. This to be sure was the employment and delight of all the leisure hours of a long life; but it is a proof what hold the memory takes, where the heart is deeply interested.
—Anne MacVicar Grant, *Poems on Various Subjects* (1803)

Piero di Cosimo (Italian, c. 1462–1521)
St. Mary Magdalene, c. 1501–1510
Oil on panel, 72.5 x 56 cm (28⁹/₁₆ x 22¹/₁₆ in.)
Palazzo Barberini, Rome

FEBRUARY

monday
4 ₃₅

tuesday
5 ₃₆

ASH WEDNESDAY

wednesday
6 ₃₇

thursday
● **7** ₃₈

friday
8 ₃₉

saturday
9 ₄₀

s	m	t	w	t	f	s
					1	2
3	4	5	6	7	8	9
10	11	12	13	14	15	16
17	18	19	20	21	22	23
24	25	26	27	28	29	

FEBRUARY

sunday
10 ₄₁

She read Dickens in the spirit in which she would have eloped with him.
—Eudora Welty, *One Writer's Beginnings* (1984)

Jean-Baptiste-Armand Guillaumin (French, 1841–1927)
Madame Guillaumin Reading, c. 1895
Oil on canvas, 73.5 x 60.5 cm (28¹⁵⁄₁₆ x 23¹³⁄₁₆ in.)
Private collection

FEBRUARY

monday
11 42

LINCOLN'S BIRTHDAY

tuesday
12 43

wednesday
13 44

VALENTINE'S DAY

thursday
☽ **14** 45

friday
15 46

saturday
16 47

s	m	t	w	t	f	s
					1	2
3	4	5	6	7	8	9
10	11	12	13	14	15	16
17	18	19	20	21	22	23
24	25	26	27	28	29	

FEBRUARY

sunday
17 48

For casual reading—in your bath, for instance, or late at night when you are too tired to go to bed, or in the odd quarter of an hour before lunch—there is nothing to touch a back number of the Girl's Own Paper.

—George Orwell, in the *Fortnightly Review,* November 1936

Alexander Mann (Scottish, 1853–1908)
Portrait of Helen Gow, n.d.
Private collection

FEBRUARY

PRESIDENTS' DAY

tuesday
19 ₅₀

wednesday
20 ₅₁

thursday
○ 21 ₅₂

friday
22 ₅₃

WASHINGTON'S BIRTHDAY

saturday
23 ₅₄

s	m	t	w	t	f	s
					1	2
3	4	5	6	7	8	9
10	11	12	13	14	15	16
17	18	19	20	21	22	23
24	25	26	27	28	29	

FEBRUARY

sunday
24 ₅₅

FEB/MAR

monday
56 25

tuesday
57 26

wednesday
58 27

thursday
59 28

friday
60 29 ☾

saturday
61 1

sunday
62 2

MOTHERING SUNDAY (UK)

MARCH

SUNDAY	MONDAY	TUESDAY	WEDNESDAY	THURSDAY	FRIDAY	SATURDAY
						1
2	3	4	5	6	7 ●	8
9	10	11	12	13	14 ☽	15
16	17	18	19	20	21 ○	22
23	24	25	26	27	28	29 ☾
30	31					

MAR 2   MOTHERING SUNDAY (UK)
MAR 8   INTERNATIONAL WOMEN'S DAY
MAR 9   DAYLIGHT SAVING TIME BEGINS
MAR 16 PALM SUNDAY

MAR 17 ST. PATRICK'S DAY
MAR 20 PURIM (BEGINS AT SUNSET)
           VERNAL EQUINOX 05:48 UT
MAR 21 GOOD FRIDAY

MAR 23 EASTER SUNDAY
MAR 24 EASTER MONDAY (CANADA, UK)
MAR 30 SUMMER TIME BEGINS (UK)

I easily sink into mere absorption of what other minds have done, and should like a whole life for that alone.
—George Eliot, in J. W. Cross, ed., *George Eliot's Life as Related in Her Letters and Journals* (1884)

Hans Olaf Heyerdahl (Norwegian, 1857–1913)
At the Window, 1881
Oil on wood block, 46 x 37 cm (18⅛ x 14⁹⁄₁₆ in.)
Nasjonalmuseet for kunst, arkitektur og design, Oslo
Photograph courtesy The Bridgeman Art Library, New York

MARCH

monday

3 ₆₃

tuesday

4 ₆₄

wednesday

5 ₆₅

thursday

6 ₆₆

friday

● **7** ₆₇

saturday

INTERNATIONAL WOMEN'S DAY

8 ₆₈

s	m	t	w	t	f	s
						1
2	3	4	5	6	7	8
9	10	11	12	13	14	15
16	17	18	19	20	21	22
23	24	25	26	27	28	29
30	31					

MARCH

DAYLIGHT SAVING TIME BEGINS

sunday

9 ₆₉

MARCH

monday
70 10

tuesday
71 11

wednesday
72 12

thursday
73 13

friday
74 14 ☽

saturday
75 15

sunday
76 16   PALM SUNDAY

MARCH

ST. PATRICK'S DAY

tuesday

18 78

wednesday

19 79

PURIM (BEGINS AT SUNSET)
VERNAL EQUINOX 05:48 UT

thursday

20 80

GOOD FRIDAY

friday

◯ **21** 81

saturday

22 82

s	m	t	w	t	f	s
						1
2	3	4	5	6	7	8
9	10	11	12	13	14	15
16	17	18	19	20	21	22
23	24	25	26	27	28	29
30	31					

MARCH

EASTER SUNDAY

sunday

23 83

All that mankind has done, thought, gained or been: it is lying as in magical preservation in the pages of books.
—Thomas Carlyle, "The Hero as Man of Letters," in *Heroes and Hero Worship* (1840)

Alfred-Émile-Léopold Stevens (Belgian, 1823–1906)
The Reader, c. 1865–1866
Oil on canvas, 66.1 x 55.3 cm (26 x 21¾ in.)
Fitzwilliam Museum, University of Cambridge, England

MARCH

EASTER MONDAY (CANADA, UK)

monday
24 84

tuesday
25 85

wednesday
26 86

thursday
27 87

friday
28 88

saturday
☾ 29 89

s	m	t	w	t	f	s
						1
2	3	4	5	6	7	8
9	10	11	12	13	14	15
16	17	18	19	20	21	22
23	24	25	26	27	28	29
30	31					

MARCH

SUMMER TIME BEGINS (UK)

sunday
30 90

He answer'd well; and much you glad mine ear,
When such accounts I of my shepherd hear:
Reading such books can raise a peasant's mind
Above a lord's who is not so inclin'd.

—Margaret Turner, *The Gentle Shepherd,*
a Scotch Pastoral . . . Attempted in English (1790)

Jean-Baptiste-Camille Corot (French, 1796–1875)
The Reader Crowned with Flowers; or, Virgil's Muse, 1845
Oil on canvas, 47 x 34 cm (18½ x 13⅜ in.)
Musée du Louvre, Paris

APRIL

SUNDAY	MONDAY	TUESDAY	WEDNESDAY	THURSDAY	FRIDAY	SATURDAY
		1	2	3	4	5
6 ●	7	8	9	10	11	12 ☽
13	14	15	16	17	18	19
20 ○	21	22	23	24	25	26
27	28 ☾	29	30			

APR 19   PASSOVER (BEGINS AT SUNSET)
APR 22   EARTH DAY

MAR/APR

monday
91 31

tuesday
92 1

wednesday
93 2

thursday
94 3

friday
95 4

saturday
96 5

sunday
97 6

APRIL

monday
7 ₉₈

tuesday
8 ₉₉

wednesday
9 ₁₀₀

thursday
10 ₁₀₁

friday
11 ₁₀₂

saturday
☽ 12 ₁₀₃

s	m	t	w	t	f	s
		1	2	3	4	5
6	7	8	9	10	11	12
13	14	15	16	17	18	19
20	21	22	23	24	25	26
27	28	29	30			

sunday
13 ₁₀₄

APRIL

Before she married, she thought she was in love; but the happiness that should have resulted from that love, somehow had not come. It seemed to her that she must have made a mistake, have misunderstood in some way or another. And Emma tried hard to discover what, precisely, it was in life that was denoted by the words "joy, passion, intoxication," which had always looked so fine to her in books.

—Gustave Flaubert, *Madame Bovary* (1857)

Carl Vilhelm Holsøe (Danish, 1863–1935)
Woman Reading in a Sunlit Room, n.d.
Private collection
Photograph courtesy Connaught Brown, London / The Bridgeman Art Library, New York

APRIL

monday
14 105

tuesday
15 106

wednesday
16 107

thursday
17 108

friday
18 109

PASSOVER (BEGINS AT SUNSET)

saturday
19 110

s	m	t	w	t	f	s
		1	2	3	4	5
6	7	8	9	10	11	12
13	14	15	16	17	18	19
20	21	22	23	24	25	26
27	28	29	30			

sunday
○ **20** 111

APRIL

It is not the volume of one's reading but the way one reads that rewards one. Those who run ahead at great speed get no rewards at all. They resemble those bees that can draw the nectar from flowers only by lying on them, not by wandering among them.

—Jeanne-Marie Bouvier de la Motte Guyon,
Le moyen court et très facile de faire oraison [The short and very easy method of prayer], (1685)

Gwendolyn Grant (Australian, 1878–1968)
Winter Sunshine, 1939
Oil on canvas, 71.8 x 61.5 cm (28¼ x 24³⁄₁₆ in.)
Queensland Art Gallery, Brisbane, Australia

APRIL

21 112

EARTH DAY
22 113

23 114

24 115

25 116

26 117

s	m	t	w	t	f	s
		1	2	3	4	5
6	7	8	9	10	11	12
13	14	15	16	17	18	19
20	21	22	23	24	25	26
27	28	29	30			

27 118

APR/MAY

monday
119 28 ☾

tuesday
120 29

wednesday
121 30

thursday
122 1

friday
123 2

saturday
124 3

sunday
125 4

MAY

SUNDAY	MONDAY	TUESDAY	WEDNESDAY	THURSDAY	FRIDAY	SATURDAY
				1	2	3
4	5 	6	7	8	9	10
11	12 ☽	13	14	15	16	17
18	19	20 ○	21	22	23	24
25	26	27	28 ☾	29	30	31

MAY 5	CINCO DE MAYO	MAY 19	VICTORIA DAY (CANADA)
	BANK HOLIDAY (UK)	MAY 26	MEMORIAL DAY OBSERVED
MAY 11	MOTHER'S DAY		BANK HOLIDAY (UK)
MAY 17	ARMED FORCES DAY	MAY 30	MEMORIAL DAY

Soon enough I had an opportunity to read my letter: my aunt fell asleep as was her wont, my uncle sat down at the harpsichord, my mother began a game of piquet with M. de Lisieux and M. Darlet, and I asked whether I might take a walk in the garden, pleading a headache. Permission was granted. While my cousins played with M. Tergi on the front steps, I rushed to the large path leading to the fields and opened the letter that follows: "No longer, my beautiful cousin, can I conceal from you the power that you have over me . . ."

—Louise Tardieu d'Esclavelles, marquise d'Épinay, *Histoire de Madame de Montbrillant* (1770)

Peter Kraemer (German, 1823–1907)
Reading the Letter [Reverie], 1887
Oil on panel, 35.6 x 28 cm (14 x 11 in.)
Josef Mensing Gallery, Hamm-Rhynern, Germany
Photograph courtesy The Bridgeman Art Library, New York

MAY

monday

CINCO DE MAYO
BANK HOLIDAY (UK)

● **5** 126

tuesday

6 127

wednesday

7 128

thursday

8 129

friday

9 130

saturday

10 131

s	m	t	w	t	f	s
				1	2	3
4	5	6	7	8	9	10
11	12	13	14	15	16	17
18	19	20	21	22	23	24
25	26	27	28	29	30	31

MAY

sunday

MOTHER'S DAY

11 132

MAY

monday
133 12

tuesday
134 13

wednesday
135 14

thursday
136 15

friday
137 16

saturday
138 17   ARMED FORCES DAY

sunday
139 18

MAY

VICTORIA DAY (CANADA)

s	m	t	w	t	f	s
				1	2	3
4	5	6	7	8	9	10
11	12	13	14	15	16	17
18	19	20	21	22	23	24
25	26	27	28	29	30	31

MAY

Sunday Morning 14th [September 1800]. Made bread. A sore thumb from a cut. A lovely day—read Boswell in the house in the morning and after dinner under the bright yellow leaves of the orchard. The pear trees a bright yellow, the apple trees green still. A sweet lovely afternoon.

—Dorothy Wordsworth, *The Grasmere Journals,* in *Journals of Dorothy Wordsworth* (1971)

Nikolay Nikolayevich Ge (Russian, 1831–1894)
Portrait of Natalia Petrunkevich, 1893
Oil on canvas, 161.8 x 114.6 cm (63¹¹⁄₁₆ x 45⅛ in.)
State Tret'yakov Gallery, Moscow

MAY/JUN

monday
MEMORIAL DAY OBSERVED
BANK HOLIDAY (UK)
26 147

tuesday
27 148

wednesday
☾ ## 28 149

thursday
29 150

friday
MEMORIAL DAY
30 151

saturday
31 152

s	m	t	w	t	f	s
1	2	3	4	5	6	7
8	9	10	11	12	13	14
15	16	17	18	19	20	21
22	23	24	25	26	27	28
29	30					

JUNE

sunday
1 153

To love these Books, and harmless Tea,
Has always been my foible,
Yet will I ne'er forgetful be
To read my Psalms and Bible

—Christian Ross Milne,
"To a Lady Who Said It Was Sinful to Read Novels,"
in *Simple Poems on Simple Subjects* (1805)

Karl Maria Schuster (Austrian, 1871–1953)
Reading on the Terrace, Capri, 1904
Oil on canvas, 90.2 x 128.3 cm (35½ x 50½ in.)
Private collection
Photograph courtesy Waterhouse and Dodd, London / The Bridgeman Art Library, New York

JUNE

SUNDAY	MONDAY	TUESDAY	WEDNESDAY	THURSDAY	FRIDAY	SATURDAY
1	2	3 ●	4	5	6	7
8	9	10 ☽	11	12	13	14
15	16	17	18 ○	19	20	21
22	23	24	25	26 ☾	27	28
29	30					

JUN 14 FLAG DAY
JUN 15 FATHER'S DAY
JUN 20 SUMMER SOLSTICE 23:59 UT

JUNE

monday

2

tuesday

3

wednesday

4

thursday

5

friday

6

saturday

7

sunday

8

JUNE

monday

9 161

tuesday

☽ **10** 162

wednesday

11 163

thursday

12 164

friday

13 165

FLAG DAY

saturday

14 166

s	m	t	w	t	f	s
1	2	3	4	5	6	7
8	9	10	11	12	13	14
15	16	17	18	19	20	21
22	23	24	25	26	27	28
29	30					

JUNE

FATHER'S DAY

sunday

15 167

A breakfast-room adjoined the drawing-room, I slipped in there. It contained a bookcase: I soon possessed myself of a volume, taking care that it should be one stored with pictures. I mounted into the window-seat: gathering up my feet, I sat cross-legged, like a Turk; and, having drawn the red moreen curtain nearly close, I was shrined in double retirement.

—Charlotte Brontë, *Jane Eyre* (1847)

Edward Burne-Jones (English, 1833–1898)
Portrait of Katie Lewis, c. 1882–1886
Oil on canvas, 61 x 127 cm (24 x 50 in.)
Private collection
Photograph courtesy Mallett Gallery, London / The Bridgeman Art Library, New York

JUNE

monday
16 ₁₆₈

tuesday
17 ₁₆₉

wednesday
○ 18 ₁₇₀

thursday
19 ₁₇₁

SUMMER SOLSTICE 23:59 UT

friday
20 ₁₇₂

saturday
21 ₁₇₃

s	m	t	w	t	f	s
1	2	3	4	5	6	7
8	9	10	11	12	13	14
15	16	17	18	19	20	21
22	23	24	25	26	27	28
29	30					

sunday
22 ₁₇₄

What counts, in the long run, is not what you read; it is what you sift through your own mind; it is the ideas and impressions that are aroused in you by your reading.

—Eleanor Roosevelt, *You Learn by Living* (1960)

Lovis Corinth (German, 1858–1925)
A Woman Reading near a Goldfish Tank, 1911
Oil on canvas, 74 x 90.5 cm (29⅛ x 35⅝ in.)
Österreichische Galerie Belvedere, Vienna
Photograph courtesy The Bridgeman Art Library, New York

JUNE

monday
23 175

tuesday
24 176

wednesday
25 177

thursday
☾ 26 178

friday
27 179

saturday
28 180

s	m	t	w	t	f	s
1	2	3	4	5	6	7
8	9	10	11	12	13	14
15	16	17	18	19	20	21
22	23	24	25	26	27	28
29	30					

sunday
29 181

*Open the book. (The gilt rubs off the edges
of the pages and pollinates the fingertips.)
Open the heavy book.*

—Elizabeth Bishop,
"Over 2,000 Illustrations and a Complete Concordance," in *A Cold Spring* (1955)

Harriet Backer (Norwegian, 1845–1932)
By Lamplight, 1890
Oil on canvas, 54.7 x 66.5 cm (21⁹⁄₁₆ x 26³⁄₁₆ in.)
Bergen Kunstmuseum, Rasmus Meyer Collection, Bergen, Norway

JULY

SUNDAY	MONDAY	TUESDAY	WEDNESDAY	THURSDAY	FRIDAY	SATURDAY
		1	2	3 ●	4	5
6	7	8	9	10 ☽	11	12
13	14	15	16	17	18 ○	19
20	21	22	23	24	25 ☾	26
27	28	29	30	31		

JUL 1   CANADA DAY (CANADA)

JUL 4   INDEPENDENCE DAY

JUL 14   BANK HOLIDAY (N. IRELAND)

JUN/JUL

monday
182 30

tuesday   CANADA DAY (CANADA)
183 1

wednesday
184 2

thursday
185 3 ●

friday   INDEPENDENCE DAY
186 4

saturday
187 5

sunday
188 6

JULY

monday
7 189

tuesday
8 190

wednesday
9 191

thursday
10 192

friday
11 193

saturday
12 194

s	m	t	w	t	f	s
		1	2	3	4	5
6	7	8	9	10	11	12
13	14	15	16	17	18	19
20	21	22	23	24	25	26
27	28	29	30	31		

JULY

sunday
13 195

Alice was beginning to get very tired of sitting by her sister on the bank and of having nothing to do: once or twice she had peeped into the book her sister was reading, but it had no pictures or conversations in it, "and what is the use of a book," *thought Alice, "without pictures or conversations?"*

—Lewis Carroll, *Alice's Adventures in Wonderland* (1865)

George Dunlop Leslie (English, 1835–1921)
Alice in Wonderland, c. 1879
Oil on canvas, 81.4 x 111.8 cm (32⅟16 x 44 in.)
Royal Pavilion, Libraries & Museums, Brighton & Hove, England
Photograph courtesy The Bridgeman Art Library, New York

JULY

BANK HOLIDAY (N. IRELAND)

monday

14 ₁₉₆

tuesday

15 ₁₉₇

wednesday

16 ₁₉₈

thursday

17 ₁₉₉

friday

○ ## 18 ₂₀₀

saturday

19 ₂₀₁

s	m	t	w	t	f	s
		1	2	3	4	5
6	7	8	9	10	11	12
13	14	15	16	17	18	19
20	21	22	23	24	25	26
27	28	29	30	31		

sunday

20 ₂₀₂

The greatest pleasures of reading consist in rereading.
—Vernon Lee, "Reading Books," *Hortus Vitae* (1904)

Jan Vermeer (Dutch, 1632–1675)
Woman Reading a Letter, c. 1662–1663
Oil on canvas, 46.5 x 39 cm (18⁵⁄₁₆ x 15³⁄₈ in.)
Rijksmuseum, Amsterdam

JULY

monday

21 203

tuesday

22 204

wednesday

23 205

thursday

24 206

friday

☾ **25** 207

saturday

26 208

s	m	t	w	t	f	s
		1	2	3	4	5
6	7	8	9	10	11	12
13	14	15	16	17	18	19
20	21	22	23	24	25	26
27	28	29	30	31		

sunday

27 209

JUL/AUG

monday

210 28

tuesday

211 29

wednesday

212 30

thursday

213 31

friday

214 1 ●

saturday

215 2

sunday

216 3

AUGUST

SUNDAY	MONDAY	TUESDAY	WEDNESDAY	THURSDAY	FRIDAY	SATURDAY
					1 ●	2
3	4	5	6	7	8 ☽	9
10	11	12	13	14	15	16 ○
17	18	19	20	21	22	23 ☾
24	25	26	27	28	29	30 ●
31						

AUG 4   CIVIC HOLIDAY (CANADA, MOST PROVINCES)

             BANK HOLIDAY (SCOTLAND)

AUG 25   BANK HOLIDAY (UK EXCEPT SCOTLAND)

AUGUST

monday

217   4

tuesday

218   5

wednesday

219   6

thursday

220   7

friday

221   8 ☽

saturday

222   9

sunday

223   10

AUGUST

monday
11 224

tuesday
12 225

wednesday
13 226

thursday
14 227

friday
15 228

saturday
◯ 16 229

s	m	t	w	t	f	s
					1	2
3	4	5	6	7	8	9
10	11	12	13	14	15	16
17	18	19	20	21	22	23
24	25	26	27	28	29	30
31						

AUGUST

sunday
17 230

A bit of trash now and then is good for the severest reader. It provides the necessary roughage in the literary diet.
—Phyllis McGinley, "New York and No Resolutions," in *Merry Christmas, Happy New Year* (1959)

Edmund Blair Leighton (English, 1853–1922)
Sweet Solitude, 1919
Oil on canvas, 35 x 37.5 cm (13¾ x 14¾ in.)
Private collection
Photograph courtesy Bonhams, London / The Bridgeman Art Library, New York

AUGUST

monday

18 231

tuesday

19 232

wednesday

20 233

thursday

21 234

friday

22 235

saturday

☾ **23** 236

sunday

24 237

s	m	t	w	t	f	s
					1	2
3	4	5	6	7	8	9
10	11	12	13	14	15	16
17	18	19	20	21	22	23
24	25	26	27	28	29	30
31						

AUGUST

We should read to give our souls a chance to luxuriate.

—Henry Miller, attributed

Georges Croegaert (Belgian, 1848–1923)
La liseuse, n.d.

BANK HOLIDAY (UK EXCEPT SCOTLAND)

monday
25 238

tuesday
26 239

wednesday
27 240

thursday
28 241

friday
29 242

saturday
● 30 243

s	m	t	w	t	f	s
					1	2
3	4	5	6	7	8	9
10	11	12	13	14	15	16
17	18	19	20	21	22	23
24	25	26	27	28	29	30
31						

sunday
31 244

POSTHUMUS: . . . A book? O rare one!
Be not, as is our fangled world, a garment
nobler than that it covers. . . .

—William Shakespeare, *Cymbeline* (c. 1609)

Sir Edward John Poynter (English, 1836–1919)
Reading, 1871
Oil on canvas
Private collection

SEPTEMBER

SUNDAY	MONDAY	TUESDAY	WEDNESDAY	THURSDAY	FRIDAY	SATURDAY
	1	2	3	4	5	6
7 ☽	8	9	10	11	12	13
14	15 ○	16	17	18	19	20
21	22 ☾	23	24	25	26	27
28	29 ●	30				

SEP 1   LABOR DAY (US, CANADA)

SEP 22   AUTUMNAL EQUINOX 15:44 UT

SEP 29   ROSH HASHANAH (BEGINS AT SUNSET)

SEPTEMBER

monday
245 1

tuesday
246 2

wednesday
247 3

thursday
248 4

friday
249 5

saturday
250 6

sunday
251 7 ☽

SEPTEMBER

s	m	t	w	t	f	s
	1	2	3	4	5	6
7	8	9	10	11	12	13
14	15	16	17	18	19	20
21	22	23	24	25	26	27
28	29	30				

SEPTEMBER

There are perhaps no days of our childhood that we lived as fully as those we imagined we had not lived at all: those we spent with a beloved book.

—Marcel Proust, *Sur la lecture* (1905)

Pierre-Auguste Renoir (French, 1841–1919)
Woman Reading, c. 1900
Oil on canvas, 56 x 46 cm (22¹⁄₁₆ x 18⅛ in.)
Tokyo Fuji Art Museum, Tokyo
Photograph courtesy The Bridgeman Art Library, New York

SEPTEMBER

monday
○ 15 259

tuesday
16 260

wednesday
17 261

thursday
18 262

friday
19 263

saturday
20 264

s	m	t	w	t	f	s
	1	2	3	4	5	6
7	8	9	10	11	12	13
14	15	16	17	18	19	20
21	22	23	24	25	26	27
28	29	30				

sunday
21 265

SEPTEMBER

Life being very short, and the quiet hours of it few, we ought to waste none of them in reading valueless books. . . . Valuable books should, in a civilized country, be within the reach of every one, printed in excellent form, for a just price . . .
—John Ruskin, "The Mystery of Life," in *Sesame and Lilies* (1868)

Frank Dicey (English, ca. 1838–1888)
The Novel, c. 1880
Oil on panel, 39.4 x 52.1 cm (15½ x 20½ in.)
Private collection
Photograph courtesy Christopher Wood Gallery, London / The Bridgeman Art Library, New York

SEPTEMBER

AUTUMNAL EQUINOX 15:44 UT

monday
☾ 22 266

tuesday
23 267

wednesday
24 268

thursday
25 269

friday
26 270

saturday
27 271

s	m	t	w	t	f	s
	1	2	3	4	5	6
7	8	9	10	11	12	13
14	15	16	17	18	19	20
21	22	23	24	25	26	27
28	29	30				

SEPTEMBER

sunday
28 272

SEP/OCT

monday

273 29 ●

tuesday

274 30

wednesday

275 1

thursday

276 2

friday

277 3

saturday

278 4

sunday

279 5

OCTOBER

SUNDAY	MONDAY	TUESDAY	WEDNESDAY	THURSDAY	FRIDAY	SATURDAY
			1	2	3	4
5	6	7 ☽	8	9	10	11
12	13	14 ○	15	16	17	18
19	20	21 ☾	22	23	24	25
26	27	28 ●	29	30	31	

OCT 8   YOM KIPPUR (BEGINS AT SUNSET)

OCT 12   COLUMBUS DAY

OCT 13   COLUMBUS DAY OBSERVED
          THANKSGIVING DAY (CANADA)

OCT 24   UNITED NATIONS DAY

OCT 26   SUMMER TIME ENDS (UK)

OCT 31   HALLOWEEN

"I had a queer time with aunt to-day, and, as I got the best of it, I'll tell you about it," began Jo, who dearly loved to tell stories. "I was reading that everlasting Belsham, and droning away as I always do, for aunt soon drops off, and then I take out some nice book, and read like fury, till she wakes up. I actually made myself sleepy; and, before she began to nod, I gave such a gape that she asked me what I meant by opening my mouth wide enough to take the whole book in at once. "'I wish I could, and be done with it,' said I, trying not to be saucy."

—Louisa May Alcott, *Little Women* (1868—1869)

Pierre-Auguste Renoir (French, 1841—1919)
Young Girl Reading, 1897
Oil on canvas, 40.5 x 28.5 cm (15¹⁵⁄₁₆ x 11¼ in.)
Photograph courtesy The Bridgeman Art Library, New York

monday

6 280

---

tuesday

☽ **7** 281

YOM KIPPUR (BEGINS AT SUNSET)

wednesday

8 282

---

thursday

9 283

---

friday

10 284

---

saturday

11 285

---

s	m	t	w	t	f	s
			1	2	3	4
5	6	7	8	9	10	11
12	13	14	15	16	17	18
19	20	21	22	23	24	25
26	27	28	29	30	31	

OCTOBER

COLUMBUS DAY

sunday

12 286

The true felicity of a lover of books is the luxurious turning of page by page, the surrender, not meanly abject, but deliber-
ate and cautious, with your wits about you, as you deliver yourself into the keeping of the book. This I call reading.
—Edith Wharton, attributed

Peder Severin Krøyer (Danish, 1851–1909)
Roses [The Artist's Wife in the Garden at Skagen], 1893
Oil on canvas

OCTOBER

COLUMBUS DAY OBSERVED
THANKSGIVING DAY (CANADA)

monday

13 287

tuesday

○ ## 14 288

wednesday

15 289

thursday

16 290

friday

17 291

saturday

18 292

s	m	t	w	t	f	s
			1	2	3	4
5	6	7	8	9	10	11
12	13	14	15	16	17	18
19	20	21	22	23	24	25
26	27	28	29	30	31	

sunday

19 293

Mr. Hurst looked at her with astonishment.
"Do you prefer reading to cards?" said he; "that is rather singular."
"Miss Eliza Bennet," said Miss Bingley, "despises cards. She is a great reader, and has no pleasure in anything else."
—Jane Austen, *Pride and Prejudice* (1813)

Jean-Georges Ferry (French, 1851–1926)
Two Women Reading in an Interior, n.d.
Private collection

OCTOBER

monday
20 294

tuesday
(21 295

wednesday
22 296

thursday
23 297

UNITED NATIONS DAY

friday
24 298

saturday
25 299

s	m	t	w	t	f	s
			1	2	3	4
5	6	7	8	9	10	11
12	13	14	15	16	17	18
19	20	21	22	23	24	25
26	27	28	29	30	31	

OCTOBER

SUMMER TIME ENDS (UK)

sunday
26 300

OCT/NOV

monday
301 27

tuesday
302 28 ⬤

wednesday
303 29

thursday
304 30

friday
305 31
HALLOWEEN

saturday
306 1

sunday
307 2
DAYLIGHT SAVING TIME ENDS

NOVEMBER

SUNDAY	MONDAY	TUESDAY	WEDNESDAY	THURSDAY	FRIDAY	SATURDAY
						1
2	3	4	5	6 ☽	7	8
9	10	11	12	13 ○	14	15
16	17	18	19 ☾	20	21	22
23	24	25	26	27 ●	28	29
30						

NOV 2   DAYLIGHT SAVING TIME ENDS   NOV 27   THANKSGIVING DAY
NOV 11   VETERANS DAY
         REMEMBRANCE DAY (CANADA)

NOVEMBER

monday

308 3

tuesday

309 4

wednesday

310 5

thursday

311 6 ☽

friday

312 7

saturday

313 8

sunday

314 9

NOVEMBER

VETERANS DAY
REMEMBRANCE DAY (CANADA)

s	m	t	w	t	f	s
						1
2	3	4	5	6	7	8
9	10	11	12	13	14	15
16	17	18	19	20	21	22
23	24	25	26	27	28	29
30						

NOVEMBER

May [1908]
I have just finished reading a book by Elizabeth Robins, Come and Find Me. *Really a clever, splendid book; it creates in me such a sense of power. I feel that I do now realise, dimly, what women in the future will be capable of. They truly as yet have never had their chance.*

—Katherine Mansfield, *The Letters and Journals of Katherine Mansfield* (1977)

Félix Vallotton (Swiss, 1865–1925)
Woman Reading, 1906
Oil on canvas, 87 x 60 cm (34¼ x 23⅝ in.)
Private collection
Photograph courtesy The Bridgeman Art Library, New York

NOVEMBER

monday
17 ₃₂₂

tuesday
18 ₃₂₃

wednesday
☽ 19 ₃₂₄

thursday
20 ₃₂₅

friday
21 ₃₂₆

saturday
22 ₃₂₇

s	m	t	w	t	f	s
						1
2	3	4	5	6	7	8
9	10	11	12	13	14	15
16	17	18	19	20	21	22
23	24	25	26	27	28	29
30						

NOVEMBER

sunday
23 ₃₂₈

She would read anything from a dictionary to a treatise on turnips. Print fascinated her, dazed her, made her good for nothing.
—Kylie Tennant, *Ride On Stranger* (1943)

Hubert Salentin (German, 1822–1910)
Relaxing after the Day's Work, n.d.
Josef Mensing Gallery, Hamm-Rhynern, Germany
Photograph courtesy The Bridgeman Art Library, New York

NOVEMBER

THANKSGIVING DAY

s	m	t	w	t	f	s
						1
2	3	4	5	6	7	8
9	10	11	12	13	14	15
16	17	18	19	20	21	22
23	24	25	26	27	28	29
30						

NOVEMBER

You should only read what is truly good or what is frankly bad.
—Gertrude Stein, quoted in Ernest Hemingway, *A Moveable Feast* (1964)

Jean-Baptiste-Armand Guillaumin (French, 1841–1927)
Madame Guillaumin Reading, c. 1887
Oil on canvas, 46.5 x 55 cm (18⁵⁄₁₆ x 21⁵⁄₈ in.)
Galerie Daniel Malingue, Paris

DECEMBER

SUNDAY	MONDAY	TUESDAY	WEDNESDAY	THURSDAY	FRIDAY	SATURDAY
	1	2	3	4	5 ☽	6
7	8	9	10	11	12 ○	13
14	15	16	17	18	19 ☾	20
21	22	23	24	25	26	27 ●
28	29	30	31			

DEC 21 HANUKKAH (BEGINS AT SUNSET)   DEC 26 BOXING DAY (CANADA, UK)
        WINTER SOLSTICE 12:04 UT   KWANZAA BEGINS
DEC 25 CHRISTMAS DAY

DECEMBER

monday

1

tuesday

2

wednesday

3

thursday

4

friday

5 ☽

saturday

6

sunday

7

DECEMBER

monday

8 343

tuesday

9 344

wednesday

10 345

thursday

11 346

friday

○ 12 347

saturday

13 348

s	m	t	w	t	f	s
	1	2	3	4	5	6
7	8	9	10	11	12	13
14	15	16	17	18	19	20
21	22	23	24	25	26	27
28	29	30	31			

DECEMBER

sunday

14 349

I am the most interesting book of all.
—Marie Bashkirtseff, *The Diary of Marie Bashkirtseff* (1997)

Marie Bashkirtseff (Ukrainian, 1858–1884)
Reading, 1880
Oil on canvas, 63 x 60.5 cm (24¹³⁄₁₆ x 23¹³⁄₁₆ in.)
Kharkov Art Museum, Kharkov, Ukraine

DECEMBER

s	m	t	w	t	f	s
	1	2	3	4	5	6
7	8	9	10	11	12	13
14	15	16	17	18	19	20
21	22	23	24	25	26	27
28	29	30	31			

DECEMBER

HANUKKAH (BEGINS AT SUNSET)
WINTER SOLSTICE 12:04 UT

Properly, we should read for power. Man reading should be man intensely alive. The book should be a ball of light in one's hand.
—Ezra Pound, *Guide to Kulchur* (1938)

August Macke (German, 1887–1914)
Elisabeth Reading, n.d.
Pfalzgalerie, Kaiserslautern, Germany
Photograph courtesy The Bridgeman Art Library, New York

DECEMBER

tuesday
23 358

wednesday
24 359

thursday
25 360

CHRISTMAS DAY

friday
26 361

BOXING DAY (CANADA, UK)
KWANZAA BEGINS

saturday
● 27 362

sunday
28 363

s	m	t	w	t	f	s
	1	2	3	4	5	6
7	8	9	10	11	12	13
14	15	16	17	18	19	20
21	22	23	24	25	26	27
28	29	30	31			

DECEMBER

DEC/JAN

monday
364 29

tuesday
365 30

wednesday
366 31

thursday   NEW YEAR'S DAY
1 1

friday   BANK HOLIDAY (SCOTLAND)
2 2

saturday
3 3

sunday
4 4 ☽

JANUARY

monday
5 ₅

tuesday
6 ₆

wednesday
7 ₇

thursday
8 ₈

friday
9 ₉

saturday
10 ₁₀

s	m	t	w	t	f	s
				1	2	3
4	5	6	7	8	9	10
11	12	13	14	15	16	17
18	19	20	21	22	23	24
25	26	27	28	29	30	31

sunday
◯ 11 ₁₁

2009

JANUARY

s	m	t	w	t	f	s
				1	2	3
4	5	6	7	8	9	10
11	12	13	14	15	16	17
18	19	20	21	22	23	24
25	26	27	28	29	30	31

FEBRUARY

s	m	t	w	t	f	s
1	2	3	4	5	6	7
8	9	10	11	12	13	14
15	16	17	18	19	20	21
22	23	24	25	26	27	28

MARCH

s	m	t	w	t	f	s
1	2	3	4	5	6	7
8	9	10	11	12	13	14
15	16	17	18	19	20	21
22	23	24	25	26	27	28
29	30	31				

APRIL

s	m	t	w	t	f	s
			1	2	3	4
5	6	7	8	9	10	11
12	13	14	15	16	17	18
19	20	21	22	23	24	25
26	27	28	29	30		

MAY

s	m	t	w	t	f	s
					1	2
3	4	5	6	7	8	9
10	11	12	13	14	15	16
17	18	19	20	21	22	23
24/31	25	26	27	28	29	30

JUNE

s	m	t	w	t	f	s
	1	2	3	4	5	6
7	8	9	10	11	12	13
14	15	16	17	18	19	20
21	22	23	24	25	26	27
28	29	30				

2009

JULY

s	m	t	w	t	f	s
			1	2	3	4
5	6	7	8	9	10	11
12	13	14	15	16	17	18
19	20	21	22	23	24	25
26	27	28	29	30	31	

AUGUST

s	m	t	w	t	f	s
						1
2	3	4	5	6	7	8
9	10	11	12	13	14	15
16	17	18	19	20	21	22
$^{23}/_{30}$	$^{24}/_{31}$	25	26	27	28	29

SEPTEMBER

s	m	t	w	t	f	s
		1	2	3	4	5
6	7	8	9	10	11	12
13	14	15	16	17	18	19
20	21	22	23	24	25	26
27	28	29	30			

OCTOBER

s	m	t	w	t	f	s
				1	2	3
4	5	6	7	8	9	10
11	12	13	14	15	16	17
18	19	20	21	22	23	24
25	26	27	28	29	30	31

NOVEMBER

s	m	t	w	t	f	s
1	2	3	4	5	6	7
8	9	10	11	12	13	14
15	16	17	18	19	20	21
22	23	24	25	26	27	28
29	30					

DECEMBER

s	m	t	w	t	f	s
		1	2	3	4	5
6	7	8	9	10	11	12
13	14	15	16	17	18	19
20	21	22	23	24	25	26
27	28	29	30	31		

2008 INTERNATIONAL HOLIDAYS

Following are the observed dates of major holidays for selected countries in 2008. Islamic observances are subject to adjustment. Holidays for the US, UK, and Canada and major Jewish holidays appear on this calendar's grid pages. Pomegranate is not responsible for errors or omissions in this list. Users of this information should confirm dates with local sources before making international travel or business plans.

ARGENTINA

1 Jan	New Year's Day
20 Mar	Holy Thursday
21 Mar	Good Friday
23 Mar	Easter
24 Mar	National Day of Memory for Truth and Justice
31 Mar	Veterans' Day/Malvinas War Memorial
1 May	Labor Day
25 May	Revolution Day
16 Jun	Flag Day
9 Jul	Independence Day
18 Aug	San Martín Day
12 Oct	Día de la Raza
8 Dec	Immaculate Conception
25 Dec	Christmas

AUSTRALIA

1 Jan	New Year's Day
28 Jan	Australia Day
3 Mar	Labor Day (WA)
10 Mar	Labor Day (Vic)
	Eight Hours Day (Tas)
17 Mar	Canberra Day (ACT)
21 Mar	Good Friday
22–24 Mar	Easter Holiday
25 Apr	Anzac Day
5 May	Labor Day (Qld)
	May Day (NT)
2 Jun	Foundation Day (WA)
9 Jun	Queen's Birthday (except WA)
4 Aug	Picnic Day (NT)
	Bank Holiday (NSW, ACT)
29 Sep	Queen's Birthday (WA)
6 Oct	Labor Day (NSW, ACT, SA)
25 Dec	Christmas
26 Dec	Boxing Day (except SA)
	Proclamation Day (SA)

BRAZIL

1 Jan	New Year's Day
20 Jan	São Sebastião Day (Rio de Janeiro)
25 Jan	São Paulo Anniversary (São Paulo)
4–5 Feb	Carnival
6 Feb	Ash Wednesday (morning only)
21 Mar	Good Friday
23 Mar	Easter
21 Apr	Tiradentes Day
1 May	Labor Day
22 May	Corpus Christi
7 Sep	Independence Day
12 Oct	Our Lady of Aparecida
2 Nov	All Souls' Day
15 Nov	Proclamation of the Republic
20 Nov	Zumbi dos Palmares Day (Rio de Janeiro)
25 Dec	Christmas

CHINA (SEE ALSO HONG KONG)

1 Jan	New Year's Day
7–9 Feb	Spring Festival/Chinese New Year
8 Mar	International Women's Day
1–3 May	Labor Day Holiday
4 May	Youth Day
1 Jun	Children's Day
1 Jul	Chinese Communist Party Founding Day
1 Aug	Army Day
1–3 Oct	National Day Holiday

FRANCE

1 Jan	New Year's Day
23–24 Mar	Easter Holiday
1 May	Labor Day
	Ascension Day
8 May	Victory Day (WWII)
11–12 May	Pentecost/Whitmonday
14 Jul	Bastille Day
15 Aug	Assumption Day
1 Nov	All Saints' Day
11 Nov	Armistice Day (WWI)
25 Dec	Christmas

GERMANY

1 Jan	New Year's Day
6 Jan	Epiphany
21 Mar	Good Friday
23–24 Mar	Easter Holiday
1 May	Labor Day
	Ascension Day
11–12 May	Pentecost/Whitmonday
22 May	Corpus Christi
15 Aug	Assumption Day
3 Oct	Unity Day
31 Oct	Reformation Day
1 Nov	All Saints' Day
19 Nov	Penance Day
24–26 Dec	Christmas Holiday
31 Dec	New Year's Eve

HONG KONG

1 Jan	New Year's Day
7–9 Feb	Spring Festival/Chinese New Year
21–24 Mar	Easter Holiday
4 Apr	Ching Ming (Tomb-Sweeping) Festival
1 May	Labor Day
12 May	Buddha's Birthday
8–9 Jun	Tuen Ng (Dragon Boat) Festival
1 Jul	Special Administrative Region Establishment Day
15 Sep	Mid-Autumn Festival
1 Oct	National Day
7 Oct	Chung Yeung Festival
25–26 Dec	Christmas Holiday

INDIA

10 Jan	Muharram (Islamic New Year)
14 Jan	Makar Sankranti
26 Jan	Republic Day
20 Mar	Prophet Muhammad's Birthday
21 Mar	Good Friday
21–22 Mar	Holi
23 Mar	Easter
14 Apr	Ramanavami
18 Apr	Mahavir Jayanti
19 May	Buddha Purnima
15 Aug	Independence Day
1 Oct	Ramzan Id (Eid-al-Fitr)
2 Oct	Mahatma Gandhi's Birthday
9 Oct	Dussehra
28 Oct	Diwali (Deepavali)
13 Nov	Guru Nanak's Birthday
8 Dec	Bakr-Id (Eid-al-Adha)
25 Dec	Christmas
29 Dec	Muharram (Islamic New Year)

IRELAND

1 Jan	New Year's Day
17 Mar	St. Patrick's Day
21 Mar	Good Friday
23–24 Mar	Easter Holiday
5 May	May Holiday
2 Jun	June Holiday
4 Aug	August Holiday
27 Oct	October Holiday
25 Dec	Christmas
26 Dec	St. Stephen's Day

ISRAEL

21 Mar	Purim
20 Apr	First day of Pesach
26 Apr	Last day of Pesach
7 May	Memorial Day
8 May	Independence Day
9 Jun	Shavuot
10 Aug	Fast of Av
30 Sep–1 Oct	Rosh Hashanah
9 Oct	Yom Kippur
14 Oct	First day of Sukkot
21 Oct	Shemini Atzeret/Simhat Torah

ITALY

1 Jan	New Year's Day
6 Jan	Epiphany
23–24 Mar	Easter Holiday
25 Apr	Liberation Day
1 May	Labor Day
2 Jun	Republic Day
29 Jun	Sts. Peter and Paul (Rome)
15 Aug	Assumption Day
1 Nov	All Saints' Day
8 Dec	Immaculate Conception
25 Dec	Christmas
26 Dec	St. Stephen's Day

2008 INTERNATIONAL HOLIDAYS

JAPAN

1 Jan	New Year's Day
14 Jan	Coming of Age Day
11 Feb	National Foundation Day
20 Mar	Vernal Equinox Holiday
29 Apr	Showa Day
3 May	Constitution Memorial Day
4 May	Greenery Day
5 May	Children's Day
21 Jul	Marine Day
15 Sep	Respect for the Aged Day
23 Sep	Autumnal Equinox Holiday
13 Oct	Health and Sports Day
3 Nov	Culture Day
24 Nov	Labor Thanksgiving Day
23 Dec	Emperor's Birthday

KENYA

1 Jan	New Year's Day
21 Mar	Good Friday
23–24 Mar	Easter Holiday
1 May	Labor Day
2 Jun	Madaraka Day
1 Oct	Eid-al-Fitr
10 Oct	Moi Day
20 Oct	Kenyatta Day
12 Dec	Jamhuri Day
25 Dec	Christmas
26 Dec	Boxing Day

MEXICO

1 Jan	New Year's Day
4 Feb	Constitution Day
17 Mar	Benito Juárez Day
21 Mar	Good Friday
23 Mar	Easter
1 May	Labor Day
5 May	Battle of Puebla (Cinco de Mayo)
16 Sep	Independence Day
1 Nov	All Saints' Day
2 Nov	Day of the Dead
17 Nov	Revolution Day
12 Dec	Our Lady of Guadalupe
25 Dec	Christmas

NETHERLANDS

1 Jan	New Year's Day
21 Mar	Good Friday
23–24 Mar	Easter Holiday
30 Apr	Queen's Birthday
1 May	Ascension Day
4 May	Remembrance Day
5 May	Liberation Day
11–12 May	Pentecost/Whitmonday
25–26 Dec	Christmas Holiday

NEW ZEALAND

1–2 Jan	New Year's Holiday
21 Jan	Provincial Anniversary (Wellington)
28 Jan	Provincial Anniversary (Auckland)
6 Feb	Waitangi Day
21 Mar	Good Friday
23–24 Mar	Easter Holiday
25 Apr	Anzac Day
2 Jun	Queen's Birthday
27 Oct	Labor Day
14 Nov	Provincial Anniversary (Canterbury)
25 Dec	Christmas
26 Dec	Boxing Day

NORWAY

1 Jan	New Year's Day
16 Mar	Palm Sunday
20 Mar	Holy Thursday
21 Mar	Good Friday
23–24 Mar	Easter Holiday
1 May	Ascension Day
	Labor Day
11–12 May	Pentecost/Whitmonday
17 May	Constitution Day
25–26 Dec	Christmas Holiday

PUERTO RICO

1 Jan	New Year's Day
6 Jan	Three Kings Day (Epiphany)
14 Jan	Eugenio María de Hostos Day
21 Mar	Good Friday
22 Mar	Emancipation Day
23 Mar	Easter
21 Apr	José de Diego Day
21 Jul	Luís Muñoz Rivera Day
25 Jul	Constitution Day
28 Jul	José Celso Barbosa Day
13 Oct	Día de la Raza
19 Nov	Discovery of Puerto Rico
27 Nov	Thanksgiving Day
25 Dec	Christmas

All US federal holidays also observed.

RUSSIA

1–5 Jan	New Year's Holiday
7 Jan	Orthodox Christmas
23 Feb	Defender of the Fatherland Day*
8 Mar	International Women's Day*
27 Apr	Orthodox Easter
1 May	Spring and Labor Day
9 May	Victory Day
12 Jun	Independence Day
4 Nov	National Unity Day

*Substitution day to be declared.

SINGAPORE

1 Jan	New Year's Day
7–8 Feb	Chinese New Year
21 Mar	Good Friday
23 Mar	Easter
1 May	Labor Day
19 May	Vesak Day (Buddha's Birthday)
9 Aug	National Day
2 Oct	Hari Raya Puasa (Eid-al-Fitr)
28 Oct	Deepavali
9 Dec	Hari Raya Haji (Eid-al-Adha)
25 Dec	Christmas

SOUTH AFRICA

1 Jan	New Year's Day
21 Mar	Good Friday
	Human Rights Day
23 Mar	Easter
24 Mar	Family Day
28 Apr	Freedom Day
1 May	Labor Day
16 Jun	Youth Day
9 Aug	National Women's Day
24 Sep	Heritage Day
16 Dec	Day of Reconciliation
25 Dec	Christmas
26 Dec	Day of Goodwill

SPAIN

1 Jan	New Year's Day
6 Jan	Epiphany
19 Mar	St. Joseph's Day
20 Mar	Holy Thursday
21 Mar	Good Friday
23 Mar	Easter
1 May	Labor Day
22 May	Corpus Christi
25 Jul	St. James the Apostle Day
15 Aug	Assumption Day
12 Oct	National Day
1 Nov	All Saints' Day
6 Dec	Constitution Day
8 Dec	Immaculate Conception
25 Dec	Christmas

SWITZERLAND

1 Jan	New Year's Day
2 Jan	Berchtold's Day
21 Mar	Good Friday
23–24 Mar	Easter Holiday
1 May	Ascension Day
	Labor Day
11–12 May	Pentecost/Whitmonday
1 Aug	National Day
25 Dec	Christmas
26 Dec	St. Stephen's Day

THAILAND

1 Jan	New Year's Day
7 Feb	Chinese New Year
21 Feb	Makha Bucha Day
7 Apr	Chakri Day
13–16 Apr	Songkran Festival
1 May	Labor Day
5 May	Coronation Day
19 May	Visakha Bucha Day (Buddha's Birthday)
18 Jul	Khao Phansa (Buddhist Lent Day)
12 Aug	Queen's Birthday
23 Oct	Chulalongkorn Day
5 Dec	King's Birthday
10 Dec	Constitution Day
31 Dec	New Year's Eve

INTERNATIONAL CALLING CODES/TIME DIFFERENCES

- From the United States, dial 011 (international access code), country code, city code, and local telephone number.
- Numbers listed alongside country names are country codes.
- Numbers listed alongside city names are city codes; an asterisk (*) means that no city code is needed.
- Numbers in parentheses indicate hourly differences from Pacific Standard Time. A range of numbers indicates a country with more than one time zone.
- Canada, US territories, and many Caribbean nations follow the North American Numbering Plan (dial 1 + 3-digit area code + local number) and are not listed here.

ALBANIA 355   (+9)
  TIRANA 4
ALGERIA 213   (+9)
  ALGIERS 2
ARGENTINA 54   (+5)
  BUENOS AIRES 11
  CÓRDOBA 351
  SANTA FÉ 342
ARMENIA 374   (+12)
  YEREVAN 10
ARUBA 297   (+4)
  ALL CITIES 8
AUSTRALIA..................... 61(+16–18)
  ADELAIDE 8
  BRISBANE 7
  CANBERRA 2
  MELBOURNE 3
  PERTH 8
  SYDNEY 2
AUSTRIA 43   (+9)
  SALZBURG 662
  VIENNA 1
BANGLADESH 880   (+14)
  CHITTAGONG 31
  DHAKA 2
BELGIUM 32   (+9)
  ANTWERP 3
  BRUSSELS 2
  GHENT 9
BOLIVIA 591   (+4)
  LA PAZ 2
  SANTA CRUZ 3
BOSNIA-HERZEGOVINA........ 387   (+9)
  SARAJEVO 33
BRAZIL .... 55 (+3–6)
  BRASÍLIA 61
  RIO DE JANEIRO 21
  SALVADOR 71
  SÃO PAULO 11
BULGARIA 359   (+10)
  SOFIA 2
CAMBODIA 855   (+15)
  PHNOM PENH 23
CAMEROON .... 237*   (+9)
CENTRAL AFRICAN REPUBLIC ..236*   (+9)
CHILE 56   (+4)
  CONCEPCIÓN 41
  SANTIAGO 2
  VALPARAÍSO 32

CHINA 86   (+16)
  BEIJING 10
  CANTON (GUANGZHOU) 20
  FUZHOU 591
  SHANGHAI 21
COLOMBIA 57   (+3)
  BOGOTÁ 1
  CALI 2
  MEDELLÍN 4
CONGO ....242*   (+9)
CONGO, DEMOCRATIC
  REPUBLIC OF 243   (+9–10)
  KINSHASA 1
COSTA RICA .... 06*   (+2)
CROATIA 385   (+9)
  DUBROVNIK 20
  ZAGREB 1
CUBA.........................53   (+3)
  GUANTÁNAMO BAY NAVAL BASE
  (FROM US ONLY) 99
  HAVANA 7
CYPRUS 357   (+10)
  NICOSIA 22
CZECH REPUBLIC 420   (+9)
  PRAGUE 2
DENMARK .... 45*   (+9)
ECUADOR 593   (+3)
  GUAYAQUIL 4
  QUITO 2
EGYPT 20   (+10)
  ALEXANDRIA 3
  CAIRO 2
EL SALVADOR ....503*   (+2)
ESTONIA 372   (+10)
  TALLINN 6
ETHIOPIA 251   (+11)
  ADDIS ABABA 11
FIJI ....679*   (+20)
FINLAND 358   (+10)
  HELSINKI 9
FRANCE 33   (+9)
  BORDEAUX 5
  MARSEILLE 491
  NICE 4
  PARIS 1
  REIMS 3
  ROUEN 2
  TOULOUSE 5
FRENCH ANTILLES ....590*   (+4)
FRENCH POLYNESIA .... 689*   (-1 – -2)
  (MOOREA AND TAHITI)
GEORGIA 995   (+12)
  TBILISI 32
GERMANY 49   (+9)
  BERLIN 30
  FRANKFURT 69
  HAMBURG 40
  MUNICH 89
GIBRALTAR .... 350*   (+9)
GREECE 30   (+10)
  ATHENS 1
  IRÁKLION (CRETE) 81

GUATEMALA 502   (+2)
  GUATEMALA CITY 2
HAITI .... 509*   (+3)
HONDURAS .... 504*   (+2)
HONG KONG .... 852*   (+16)
HUNGARY..................... 36   (+9)
  BUDAPEST 1
  DEBRECEN 52
ICELAND .... 354*   (+8)
INDIA 91   (+13.5)
  BANGALORE 80
  BOMBAY (MUMBAI) 22
  CALCUTTA 33
  MADRAS 44
  NEW DELHI 11
INDONESIA .... 62(+15–17)
  JAKARTA 21
IRAN 98   (+11.5)
  ESFAHAN 311
  SHIRAZ 711
  TEHRAN 211
IRAQ 964   (+11)
  BAGHDAD 1
  BASRA 40
  KIRKUK 50
  MOSUL 60
IRELAND 353   (+8)
  CORK 21
  DUBLIN 1
ISRAEL 972   (+10)
  HAIFA 4
  JERUSALEM 2
  TEL AVIV 3
ITALY 39   (+9)
  FLORENCE 055
  GENOA 010
  MILAN 02
  NAPLES 081
  ROME 06
  VENICE 041
IVORY COAST ....225*   (+8)
JAPAN 81   (+17)
  KYOTO 75
  TOKYO 3
  YOKOHAMA 45
JORDAN.......................962   (+10)
  AMMAN 6
  KARAK 3
KENYA..................... 254   (+11)
  MOMBASA 11
  NAIROBI 2
N. KOREA 850   (+17)
S. KOREA 82   (+17)
  KWANGJU 62
  PUSAN 51
  SEOUL 2
  TAEGU 53
KUWAIT .... 965*   (+11)
LAOS 856   (+15)
  VIENTIANE 21

LATVIA 371   (+10)
  RIGA 2
LEBANON 961   (+10)
  BEIRUT 1
LIBERIA . . . . 231*   (+8)
LIBYA. 218   (+10)
  TRIPOLI 21
LIECHTENSTEIN . . . . 423*   (+9)
LITHUANIA 370   (+10)
  KAUNAS 37
LUXEMBOURG . . . . 352*   (+9)
MACAU . . . . 853*   (+16)
MACEDONIA 389   (+9)
MALAYSIA 60   (+16)
  IPOH 5
  KUALA LUMPUR 3
MEXICO .52 (+0–2)
  ACAPULCO 744
  CABO SAN LUCAS 624
  CANCÚN 998
  CIUDAD JUÁREZ 656
  ENSENADA 646
  GUADALAJARA 33
  LA PAZ 612
  MAZATLÁN 669
  MEXICALI 686
  MEXICO CITY 55
  MONTERREY 81
  TIJUANA 664
  VERACRUZ 229
MONACO . . . . 377*   (+9)
MOROCCO 212   (+8)
  MARRAKECH 44
  RABAT 37
MOZAMBIQUE 258   (+10)
  MAPUTO 1
MYANMAR .95 (+14.5)
  RANGOON (YANGON) 1
NAMIBIA. 264   (+9)
  WINDHOEK 61
NEPAL. 977   (+14)
  KATHMANDU 1
NETHERLANDS 31   (+9)
  AMSTERDAM 20
  THE HAGUE (DEN HAAG) 70
  ROTTERDAM 10
NETHERLANDS ANTILLES. 599   (+4)
  CURAÇAO 9
  ST. MAARTEN 5
NEW ZEALAND . . . . 64 (+20–21)
  AUCKLAND 9
  CHRISTCHURCH 3
  WELLINGTON 4
NICARAGUA 505   (+2)
  LEÓN 311
  MANAGUA 2
NIGERIA 234   (+9)
  LAGOS 1
NORWAY . . . . 47*   (+9)
PAKISTAN. 92   (+13)
  ISLAMABAD 51
  KARACHI 21
  LAHORE 42
PANAMA. . . . . 507*   (+3)

PARAGUAY 595   (+4)
  ASUNCIÓN 21
  CONCEPCIÓN 31
PERU. 51   (+3)
  AREQUIPA 54
  LIMA 1
PHILIPPINES. 63   (+16)
  BACOLOD 34
  CEBU CITY 32
  DAVAO 82
  ILOILO CITY 33
  MANILA 2
POLAND 48   (+9)
  GDANSK 58
  KRAKOW 12
  WARSAW 22
PORTUGAL. 351   (+8)
  LISBON 21
ROMANIA. 40   (+10)
  BUCHAREST 21
RUSSIA . . . . 7 (+10–20)
  MOSCOW 495
  ST. PETERSBURG 812
SAUDI ARABIA 966   (+11)
  JEDDAH 2
  MECCA (MAKKAH) 2
  RIYADH 1
SENEGAL. . . . . 221*   (+8)
SERBIA AND MONTENEGRO 381   (+9)
  BELGRADE 11
  CETINJE 86
SINGAPORE . . . . 65*   (+16)
SLOVAKIA. 421   (+9)
  BRATISLAVA 2
SLOVENIA 386   (+9)
  LJUBLJANA 1
  MARIBOR 2
SOUTH AFRICA 27   (+10)
  BLOEMFONTEIN 51
  CAPE TOWN 21
  DURBAN 31
  JOHANNESBURG 11
  PRETORIA 12
SPAIN 34   (+9)
  BARCELONA 93
  GRANADA 958
  MADRID 91
  PALMA DE MALLORCA 971
  PAMPLONA 948
  SEVILLE 95
  VALENCIA 96
SRI LANKA. 94   (+14)
  COLUMBO CENTRAL 1
SURINAME . . . . .597*   (+5)
SWEDEN 46   (+9)
  MALMO 40
  STOCKHOLM 8
SWITZERLAND 41   (+9)
  BASEL 61
  BERNE 31
  GENEVA 22
  LAUSANNE 21
  LUCERNE 41
  ZÜRICH 1

SYRIA 963   (+10)
  DAMASCUS 11
TAIWAN 886   (+16)
  KAO-HSIUNG 7
  TAINAN 6
  TAIPEI 2
TANZANIA 255   (+11)
  DAR ES SALAAM 22
  TANGA 27
THAILAND 66   (+15)
  BANGKOK 2
  CHANTHABURI 39
TUNISIA .216   (+9)
  BIZERTE 2
  TUNIS 1
TURKEY 90   (+10)
  ANKARA 312
  ISTANBUL
    ASIAN 216
    EUROPEAN 212
UGANDA. 256   (+11)
  ENTEBBE 42
  KAMPALA 41
UKRAINE .380   (+10)
  DONETSK 62(2)
  KIEV 44
  LVOV 32(2)
UNITED ARAB EMIRATES. 971   (+12)
  ABU DHABI 2
  AJMAN 6
  AL AIN 3
  FUJAIRAH 9
UNITED KINGDOM 44   (+8)
  BELFAST 28
  BIRMINGHAM 121
  CARDIFF 29
  EDINBURGH 131
  GLASGOW 141
  LIVERPOOL 151
  LONDON 20
  MANCHESTER 161
  SOUTHAMPTON 23
URUGUAY. 598   (+5)
  CANELONES 33
  MERCEDES 53
  MONTEVIDEO 2
VATICAN CITY 39   (+9)
  ALL POINTS 6
VENEZUELA 58   (+4)
  CARACAS 212
  MARACAIBO 261
  MARACAY 243
  VALENCIA 241
VIETNAM 84   (+15)
  HANOI 4
  HO CHI MINH CITY 8
YEMEN 967   (+11)
  ADEN 2
  SANA'A 1
  ZABID 3
ZAMBIA 260   (+10)
  LUSAKA 1
ZIMBABWE. 263   (+10)
  HARARE 4

NOTES

PERSONAL INFORMATION

name _____ _____

address _____

city _____ state _____ zip _____

phone _____

cell/pgr _____ fax _____

e-mail _____

in case of emergency, please notify:

name _____

address _____

city _____ state _____ zip _____

phone _____

physician's name _____

physician's phone _____

health insurance company _____

plan number _____

allergies _____

other _____

driver's license number _____

car insurance company _____

policy number _____